ADIOS

English Words: Eddie Woods.
Music & Spanish Words: Enric Madriguera.

A DREAM IS A WISH YOUR HEART MAKES

Words & Music: Mack David, Al Hoffman and Jerry Livingston.

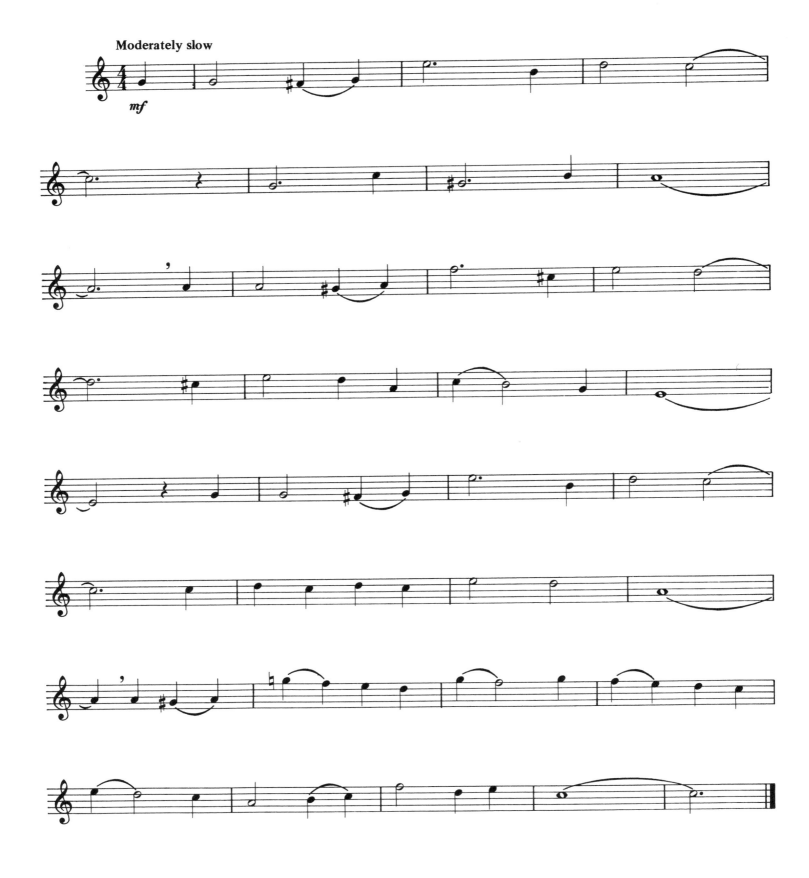

CLARINET
ONE HUNDRED & ONE
SOLOS

Designed by Pearce Marchbank Studio.
Cover photography by Rod Shone.

This book © Copyright 1986 by
Wise Publications
UK ISBN 0.7119.0852.4
UK Order No. AM 62225

Exclusive Distributors:
Music Sales Limited
8/9 Frith Street, London W1V 5TZ, England.
Music Sales Pty. Limited
120 Rothschild Avenue, Rosebery, NSW 2018, Australia.

Music Sales complete catalogue lists thousands of
titles and is free from your local music book shop,
or direct from Music Sales Limited.
Please send £1 in stamps for postage to
Music Sales Limited, 8/9 Frith Street, London W1V 5TZ.

Printed and bound in Great Britain by
Courier International Ltd, Tiptree, Essex

Wise Publications
London/New York/Sydney/Cologne.

ALICE BLUE GOWN

Words: Joseph McCarthy.
Music: Harry Tierney.

ALLEGRO

By: Franz Joseph Haydn.

ALL SHOOK UP

Words & Music: Otis Blackwell and Elvis Presley.

A MAN AND A WOMAN
(Un Homme Et Une Femme)

Music: Francis Lai.
Original Words: Pierre Barouh.
English Lyric: Jerry Keller.

A MUSICAL JOKE

By: Wolfgang Amadeus Mozart.

AN APPLE FOR THE TEACHER

Words: Johnny Burke.
Music: James V. Monaco.

AT SEVENTEEN

Words & Music: Janis Ian.

BARCAROLLE (from ''The Tales of Hoffmann'')

By: Jacques Offenbach.

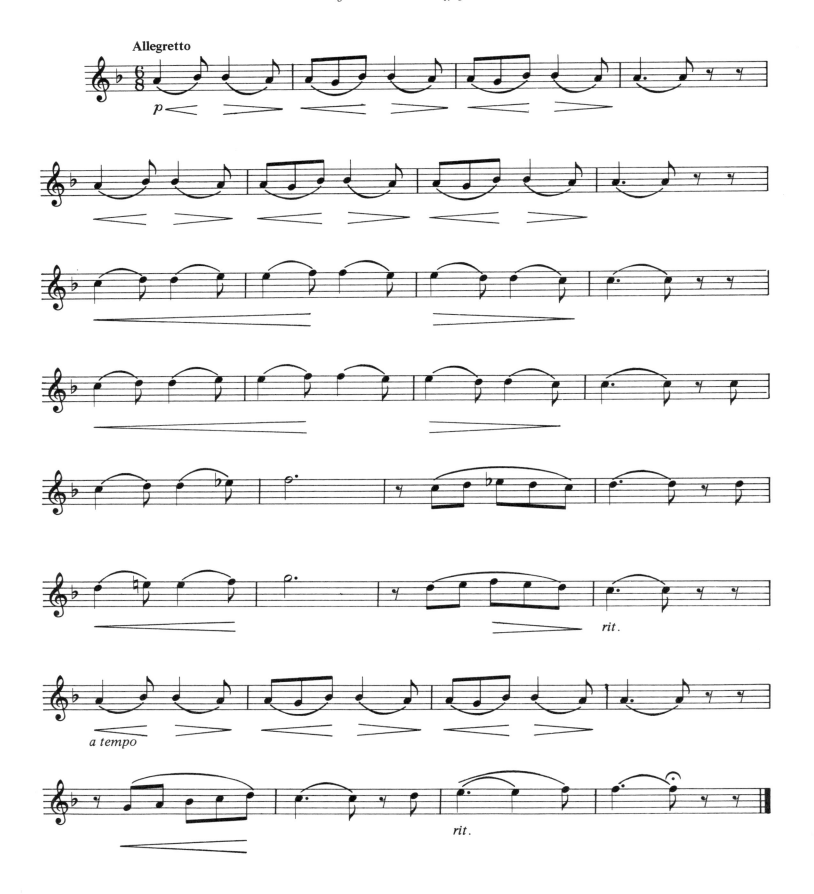

BE-BOP-A-LULA

Words & Music: Gene Vincent and Sheriff Tex Davis.

BECAUSE OF YOU

Words & Music: Arthur Hammerstein and Dudley Wilkinson.

BIG SPENDER

Words: Dorothy Fields.
Music: Cy Coleman.

BLUE DANUBE

By: Johann Strauss Jr.

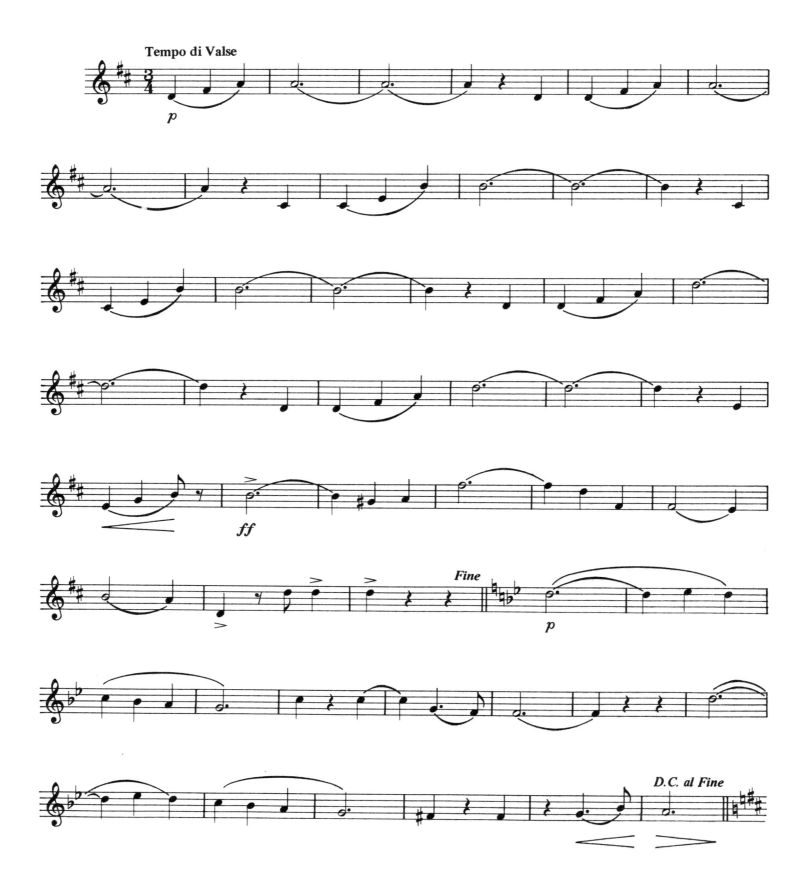

BLUE EYES CRYING IN THE RAIN

Words & Music: Fred Rose.

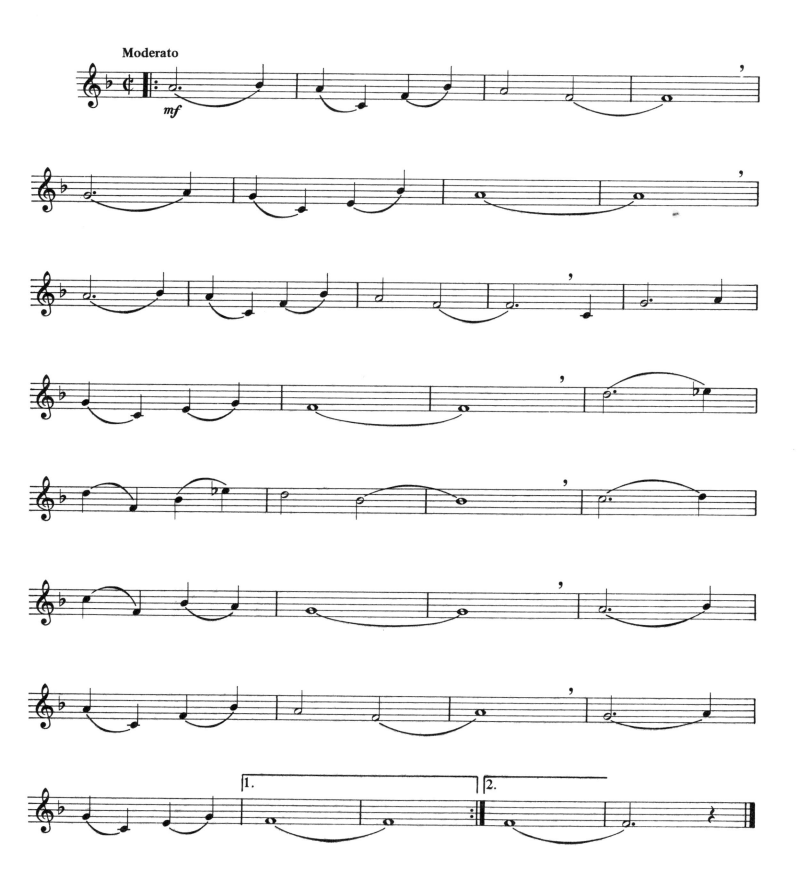

BLUE SUEDE SHOES

Words & Music: Carl Lee Perkins.

BRIDGE OVER TROUBLED WATER

Words & Music: Paul Simon.

BY THE FIRESIDE

Words & Music: Ray Noble, Jimmy Campbell and Reg Connelly.

CRUISING DOWN THE RIVER

Words & Music: Eily Beadell and Nell Tollerton.

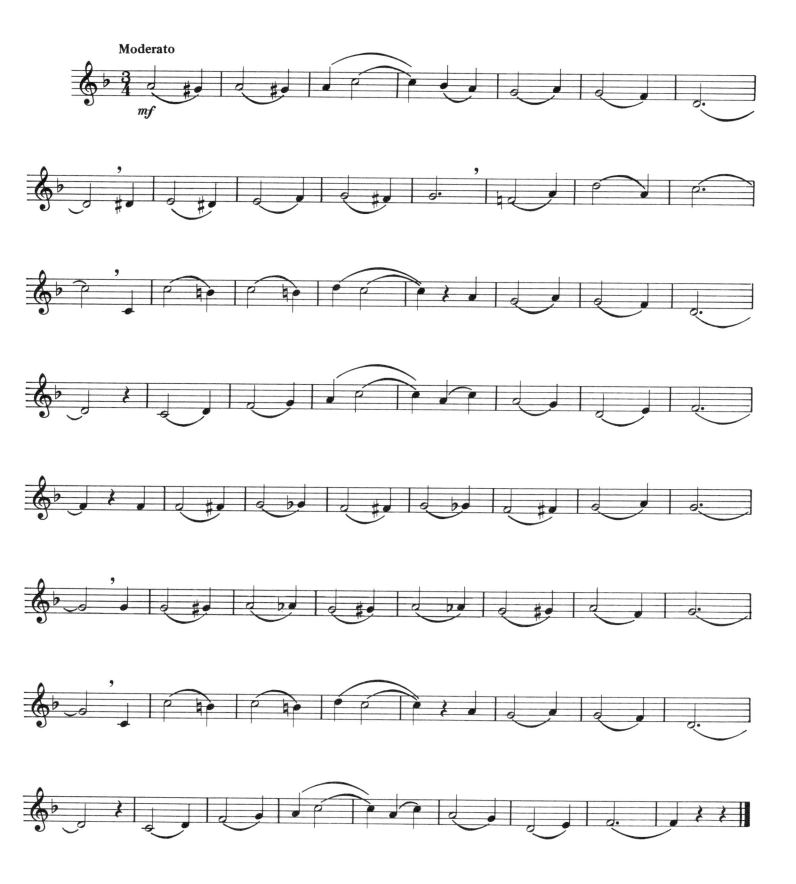

DAYTIME FRIENDS

Words & Music: Ben Peters.

Moderately (not too slow)

DER LINDENBAUM (The Lime Tree)

By: Franz Schubert.

DREAMING

Words & Music: Bud Flanagan and Reg Connelly.

DRIFTING AND DREAMING (Sweet Paradise)

Words: Haven Gillespie.
Music: Egbert Van Alstyne, Erwin R. Schmidt and Loyal Curtis.

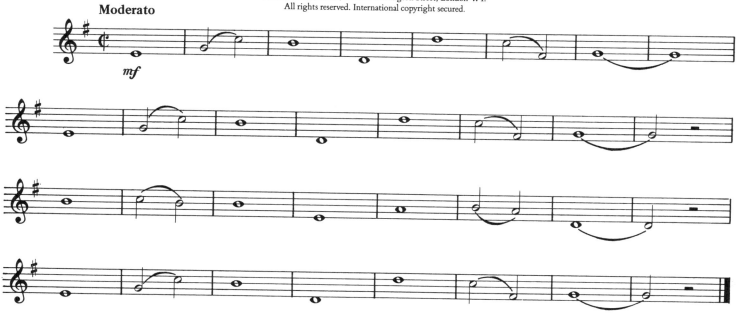

EAST OF THE SUN (And West Of The Moon)

Words & Music: Brooks Bowman.

EL CONDOR PASA (If I Could)

Musical Arrangement: J. Milchberg and D. Robles.
English Lyric: Paul Simon.

ELEANOR RIGBY

Words & Music: John Lennon and Paul McCartney.

FALLING IN LOVE AGAIN

Music & Original Words: Friedrich Hollander.
English Words: Reg Connelly.

FEELS LIKE I'M IN LOVE

Words & Music: Ray Dorset.

HONEYSUCKLE ROSE

Music: Thomas 'Fats' Waller.
Words: Andy Razaf.

HOMEWARD BOUND

Words & Music: Paul Simon.

HORNPIPE

By: Henry Purcell.

IF I HAD YOU

Words & Music: Ted Shapiro, Jimmy Campbell and Reg Connelly.

I'LL ALWAYS BE IN LOVE WITH YOU

Words & Music: Herman Ruby and Green & Stept.

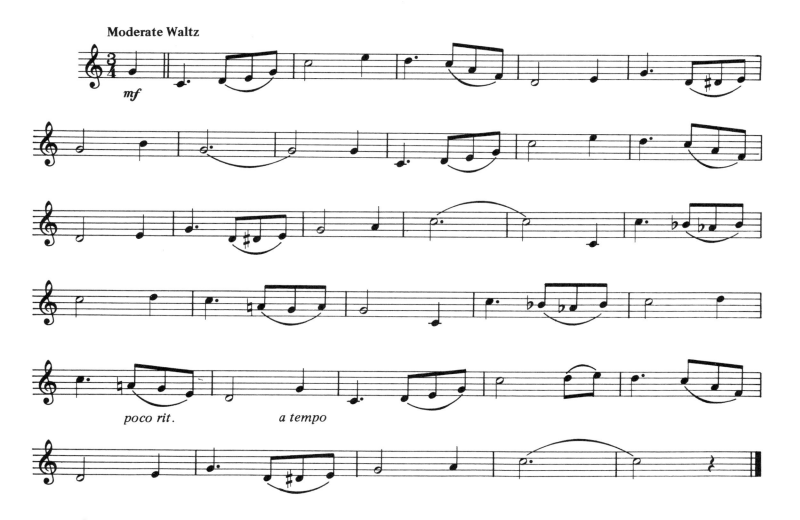

I'D DO ANYTHING

Words & Music: Lionel Bart.

IN THE CHAPEL IN THE MOONLIGHT

Words & Music: Billy Hill.

I WANNA BE LIKE YOU

Words & Music: Richard M. Sherman and Robert B. Sherman.

Brightly

I LEFT MY HEART IN SAN FRANCISCO

Words: Douglas Cross.
Music: George Cory.

I'M GETTIN' SENTIMENTAL OVER YOU

Words: Ned Washington. Additional Words: Reg Howard.
Music: Geo. Bassman.

JOLENE

Words & Music: Dolly Parton.

KNOWING ME, KNOWING YOU

Words & Music: Benny Andersson, Stig Anderson and Bjorn Ulvaeus.

LET IT BE ME (Je t'appartiens)

Music: Gilbert Becaud.
Original Words: Pierre Delanoe.
English Lyric: Mann Curtis.

Moderately

A LITTLE CO-OPERATION FROM YOU

Words & Music: Samuel Lerner, Al Goodhart and Al Hoffman.

LITTLE GIRL

Words & Music: Madeline Hyde and Francis Henry.

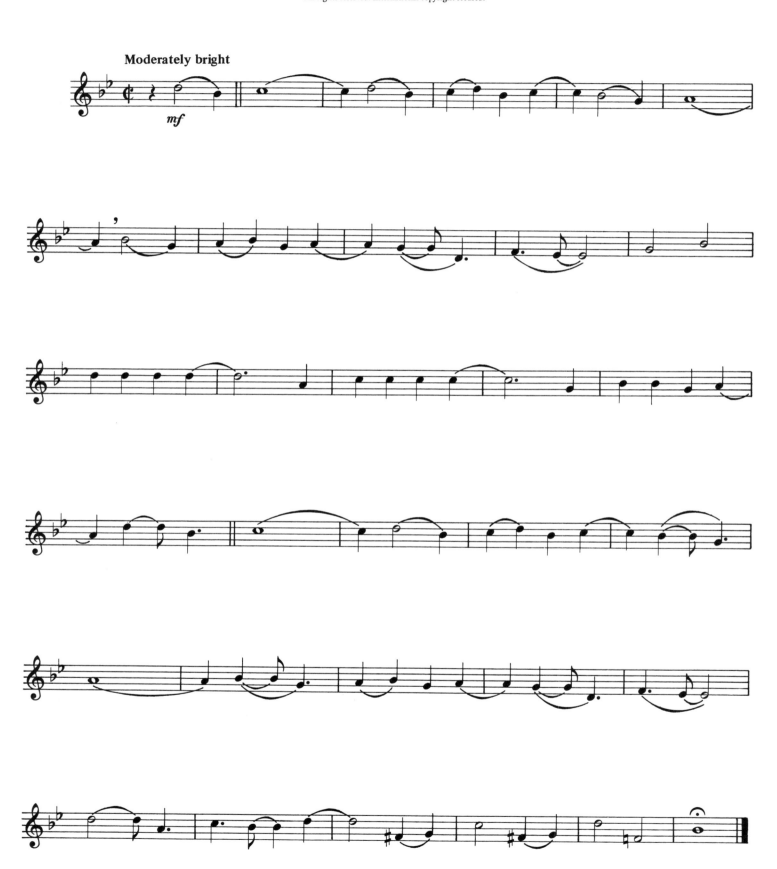

LOUISE

Words: Leo Robin.
Music: Richard A. Whiting.

LOVE IS A SONG

Words: Larry Morey.
Music: Frank Churchill.

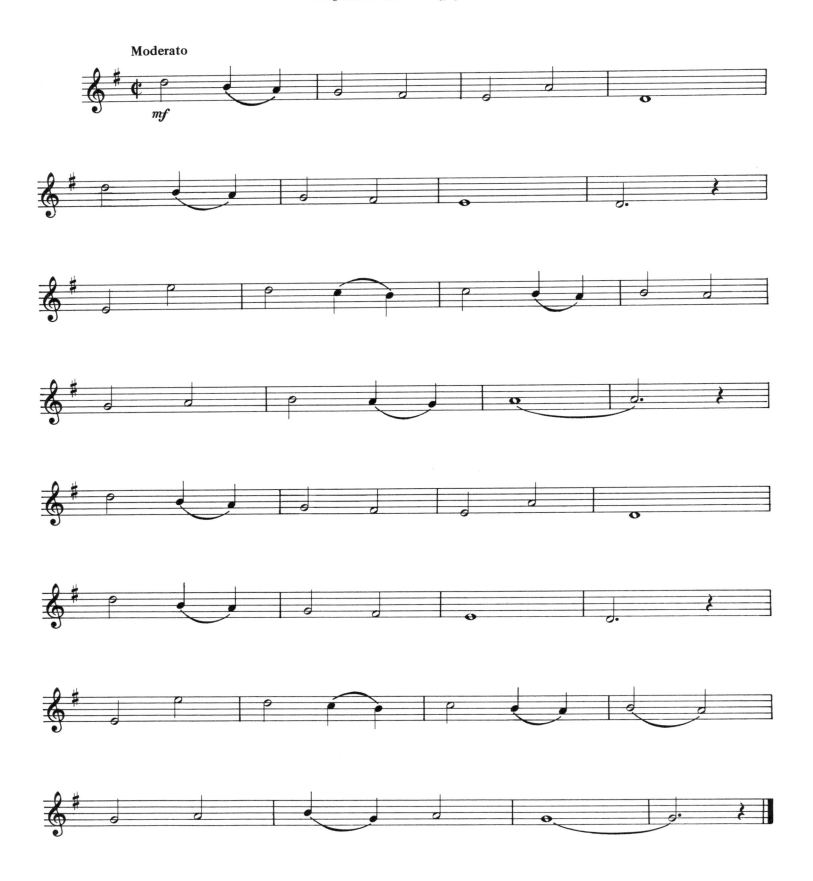

MALAGUENA

English Words: George Brown.
Music: Ernesto Lecuona.

LOVE'S ROUNDABOUT (La Ronde De L'Amour)

French Words: Louis Ducreux.
English Words: Harold Purcell.
Music: Oscar Straus.

Waltz tempo

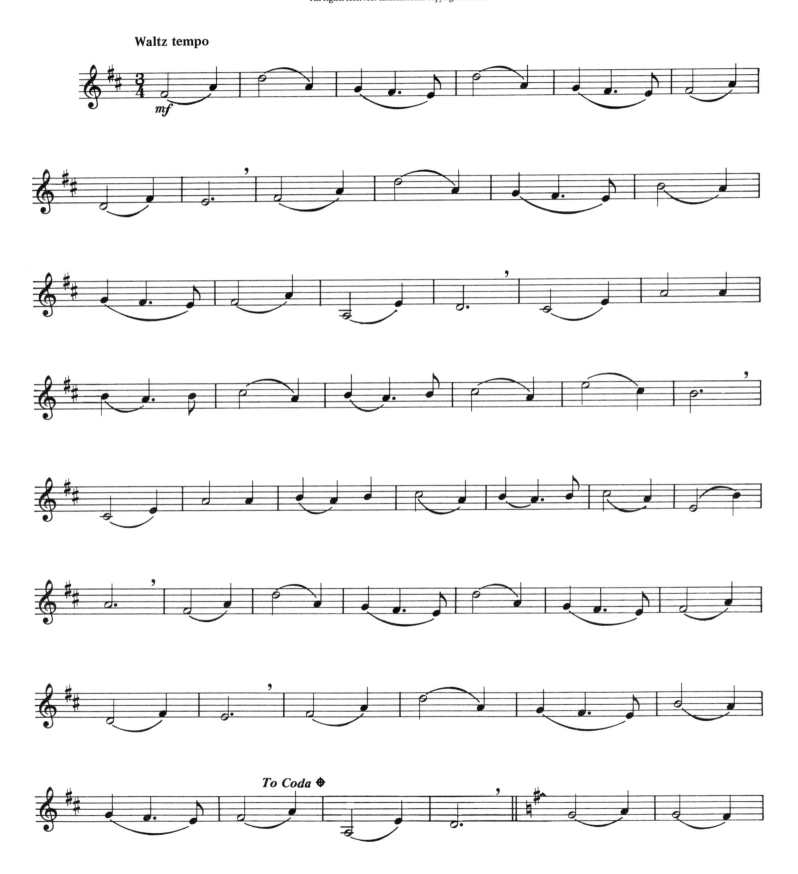

THE LONESOME ROAD

Words: Gene Austin.
Music: Nathaniel Shilkret.

Moderato

LOVE THEME (from ''Romeo and Juliet'')

By: Peter Ilyich Tchaikovsky.

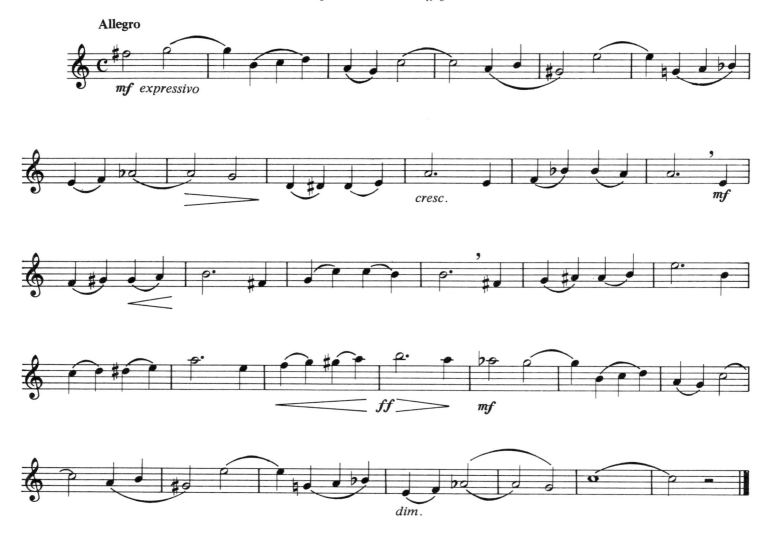

MARCH

By: Johann Sebastian Bach.

MELODY OF LOVE

Words: Tom Glazer.
Music: H. Engelmann.

Slow Waltz

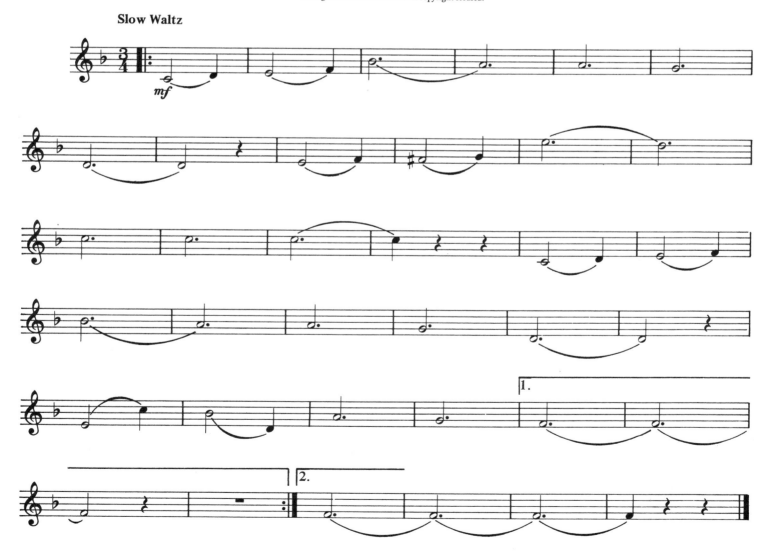

MIDNIGHT SUN

Words: Johnny Mercer.
Music: Sonny Burke and Lionel Hampton.

MINUET

By: George Frideric Handel.

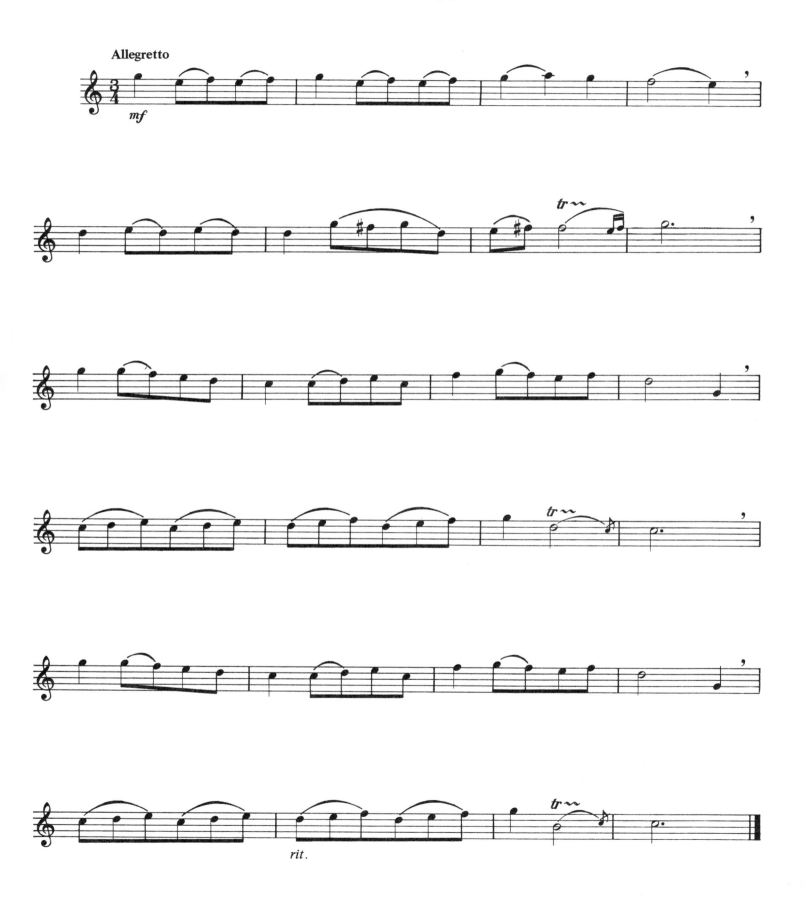

MRS ROBINSON

Words & Music: Paul Simon.

THE MUSIC GOES 'ROUND AND AROUND

Words: "Red" Hodgson.
Music: Edward Farley and Michael Riley.

MY VERY GOOD FRIEND THE MILKMAN

Words: Johnny Burke.
Music: Harold Spina.

NELLIE THE ELEPHANT

Words: Ralph Butler.
Music: Peter Hart.

OB-LA-DI, OB-LA-DA

Words & Music: John Lennon and Paul McCartney.

NONE BUT THE LONELY HEART
(Mignon's Song)

By: Peter Ilyich Tchaikovsky.

Andante non tanto

ON WINGS OF SONG

By: Felix Mendelssohn.

O SOLE MIO

By: E. Di Capua.

ON THE CREST OF A WAVE

Words & Music: Ralph Reader.

PIANO MAN

Words & Music: Billy Joel.

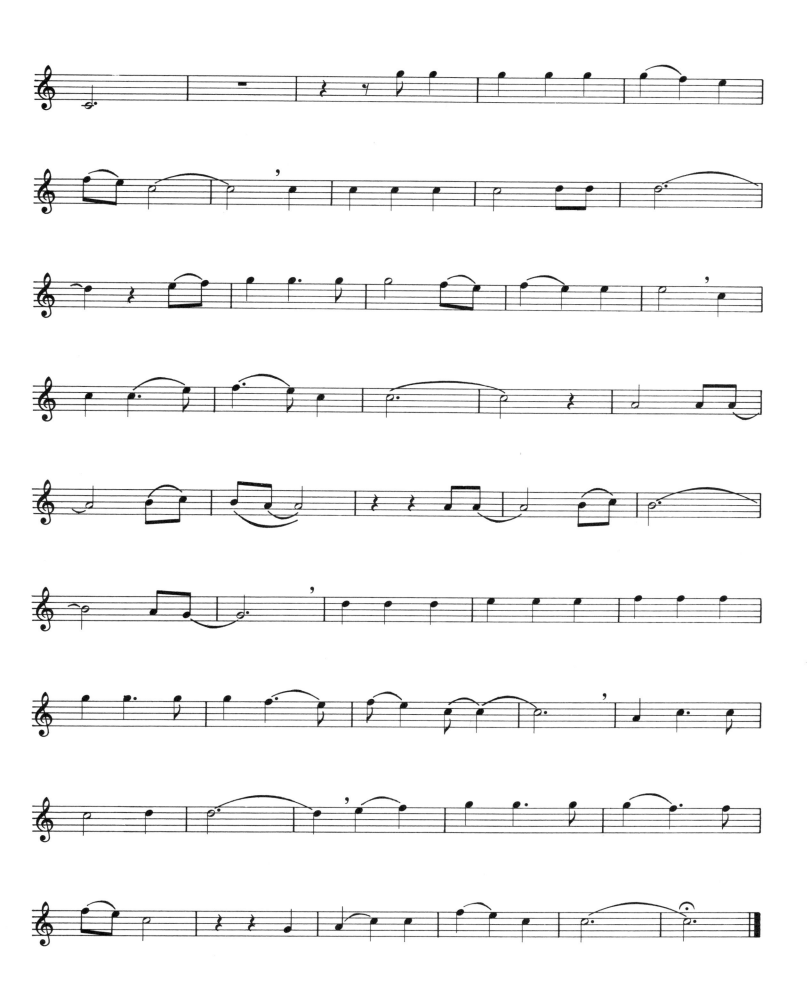

PENNY LANE

Words & Music: John Lennon and Paul McCartney.

PERDIDO

Music: Juan Tizol.
Words: Harry Lenk and Ervin Drake.

PIGALLE

English Words: Reg Connelly.
French Words: Geo. Koger.
Music: Georges Ulmer and Guy Luypaerts.

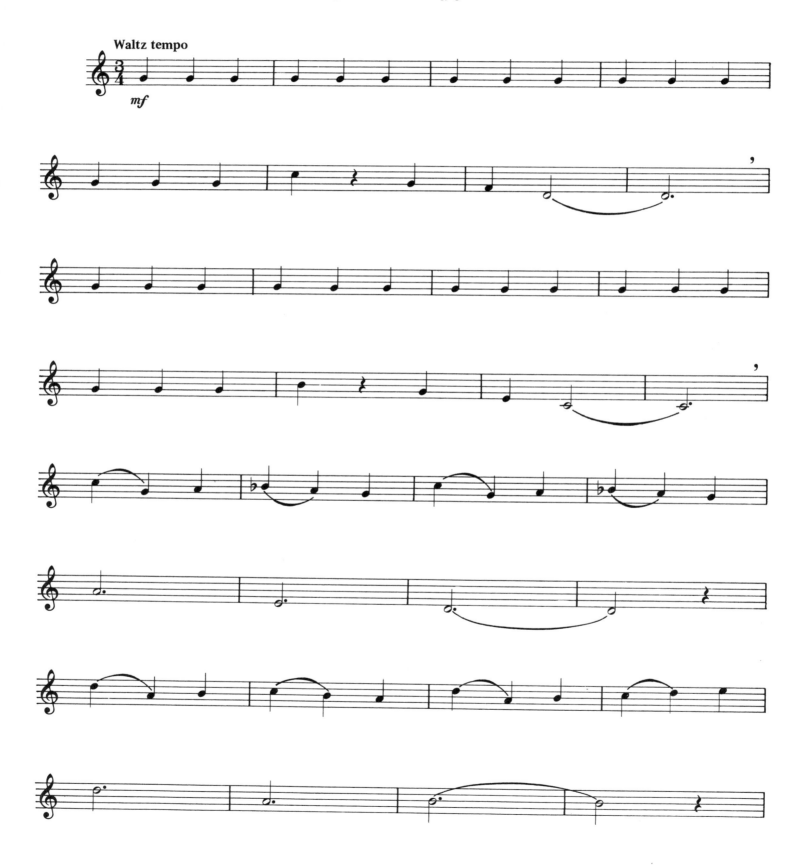

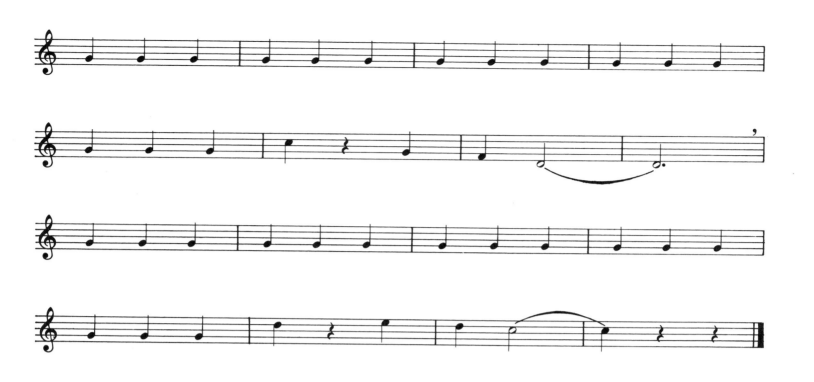

SATIN DOLL

Words: Johnny Mercer.
Music: Duke Ellington and Billy Strayhorn.

SHOW ME THE WAY TO GO HOME

Words & Music: Irving King.

SLAVONIC DANCE

By: Antonin Dvořák.

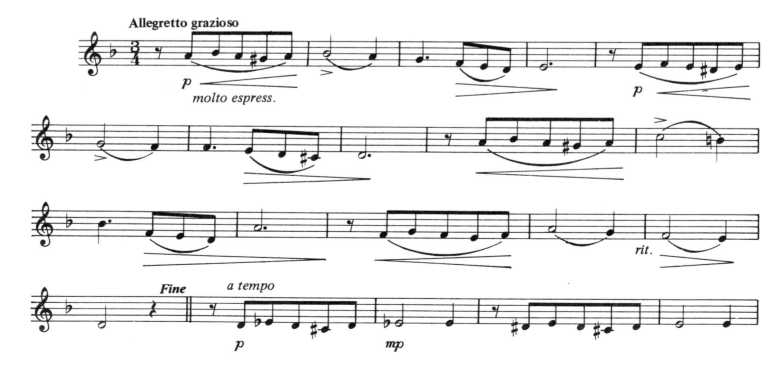

SIXTEEN TONS

Words & Music: Merle Travis.

SANTA LUCIA

Traditional.

SNOOTIE LITTLE CUTIE

Words & Music: Bob Troup.

SOMETHIN' STUPID

Words & Music: C. Carson Parks.

SOMETIMES WHEN WE TOUCH

Words & Music: Dan Hill and Barry Mann.

SO TIRED

Words & Music: Russ Morgan and Jack Stuart.

THE SOUND OF SILENCE

Words & Music: Paul Simon.

STRANGERS IN THE NIGHT

Music: Bert Kaempfert.
Words: Charles Singleton and Eddie Snyder.

STARS FELL ON ALABAMA

Words: Mitchell Parish.
Music: Frank Perkins.

SPANISH EYES

Words: Charles Singleton & Eddie Snyder.
Music: Bert Kaempfert.

SWEET LEILANI

Words & Music: Harry Owens.

SWEET SUE – JUST YOU

Words: Will J. Harris.
Music: Victor Young.

Moderato

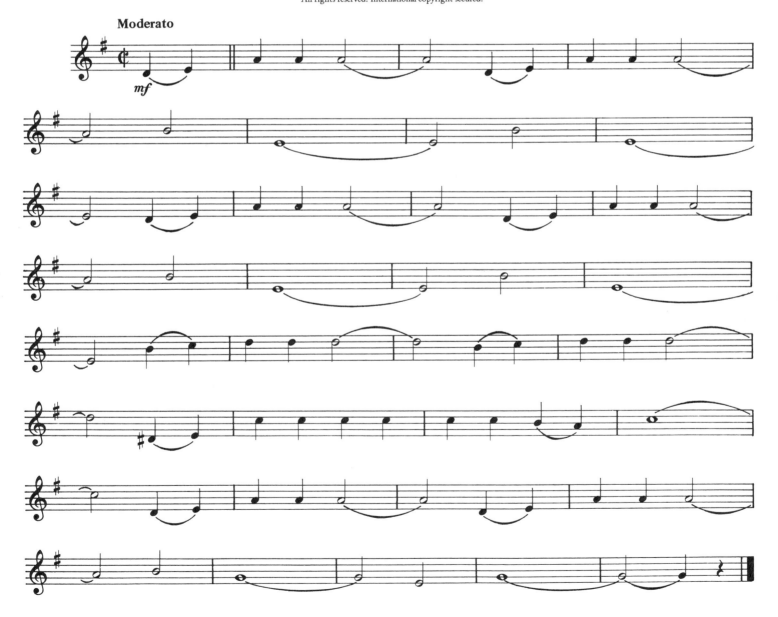

TENNESSEE WALTZ

Words & Music: Redd Stewart and Pee Wee King.

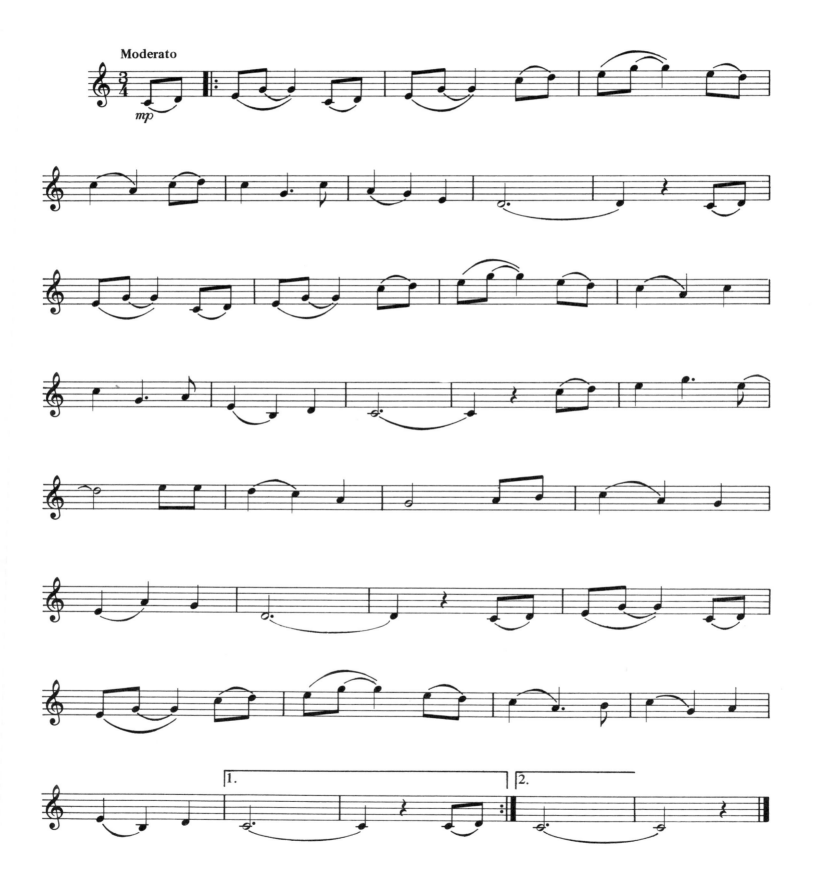

TIME ON MY HANDS

Words: Harold Adamson and Mack Gordon.
Music: Vincent Youmans.

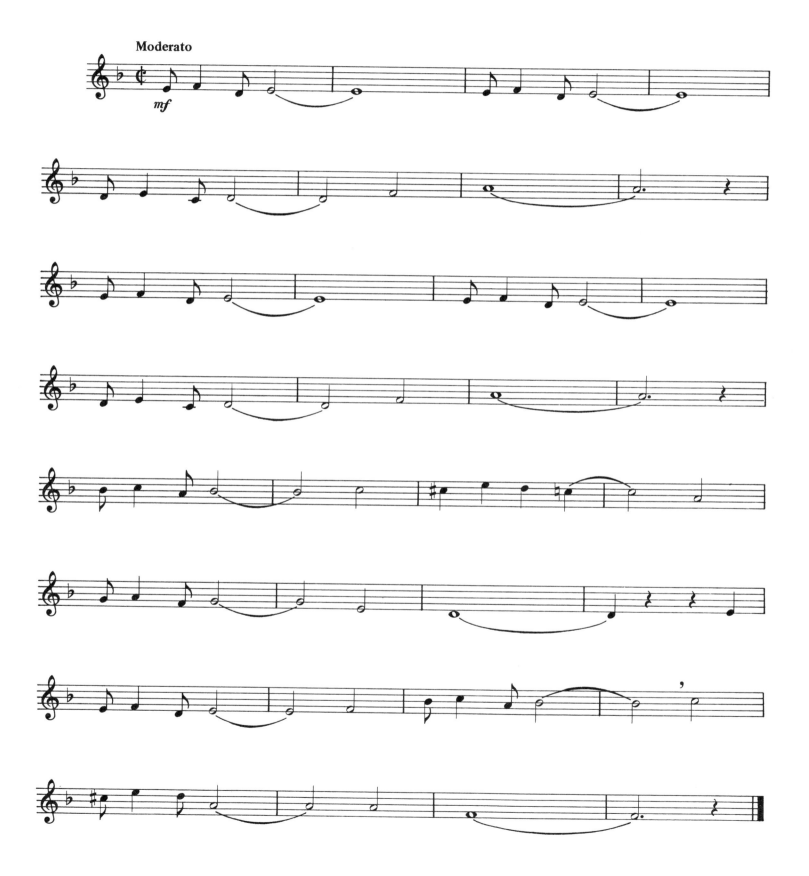

TOREADOR'S SONG (from ''Carmen'')

By: Georges Bizet.

TAKE THE 'A' TRAIN

Words & Music: Billy Strayhorn.

THE TOUCH OF YOUR LIPS

Words & Music: Ray Noble.

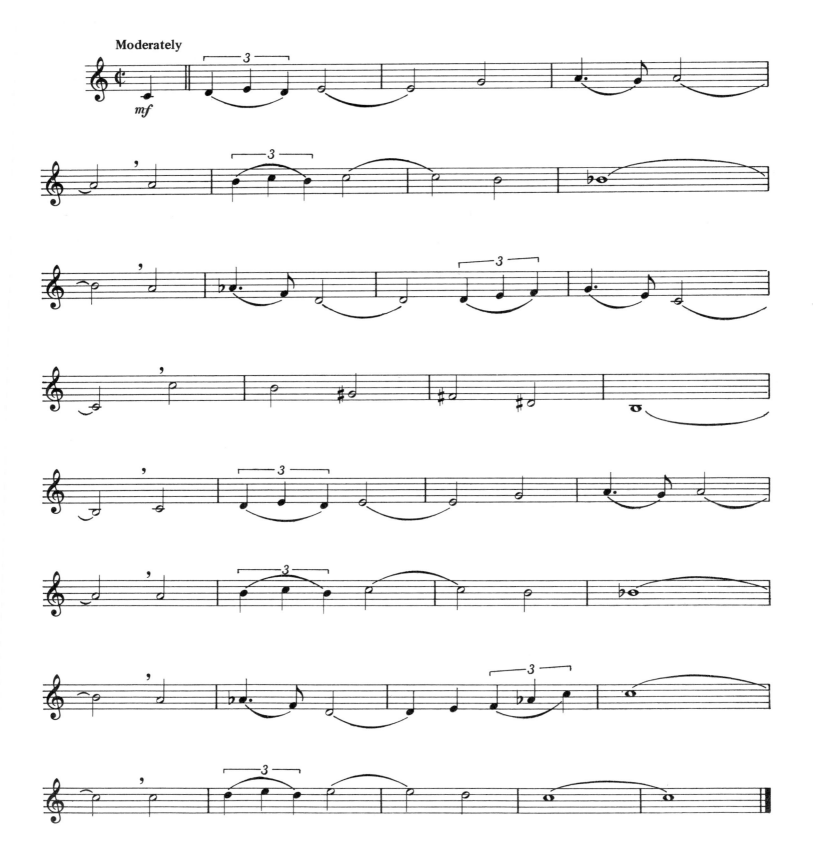

TRY A LITTLE TENDERNESS

Words & Music: Harry Woods, Jimmy Campbell and Reg Connelly.

TULIPS FROM AMSTERDAM

English Words: Gene Martyn.
Original Words: Neumann and Bader.
Music: Ralf Arnie.

Quick Waltz tempo

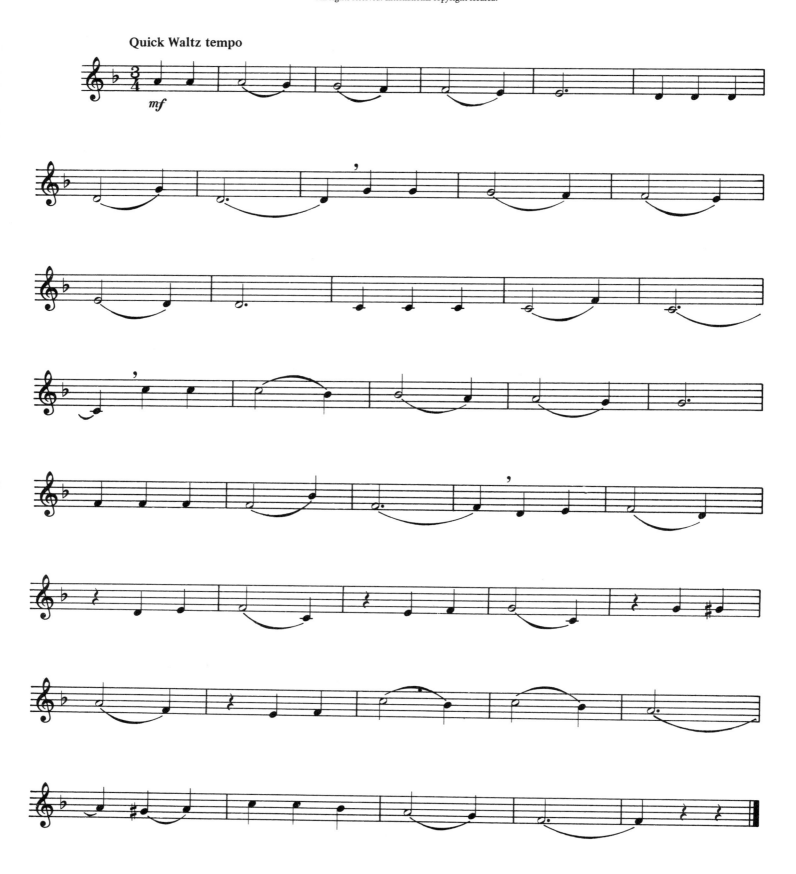

UNDERNEATH THE ARCHES

Words & Music: Bud Flanagan (Additional words: Reg Connelly).

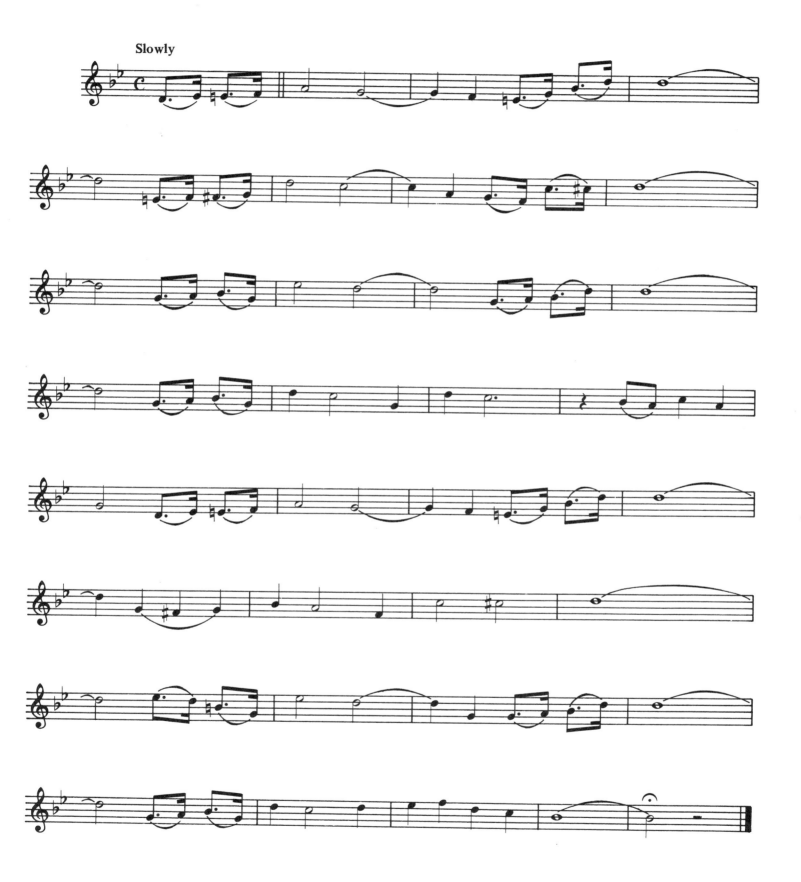

UNDER PARIS SKIES
(Sous Le Ciel De Paris)

Words: Kim Gannon.
Music: Hubert Giraud.

Moderate Waltz tempo

poco rit.

THE VERY THOUGHT OF YOU

Words & Music: Ray Noble.

Moderato

WOODEN HEART

Words & Music: Fred Wise, Ben Weisman, Kay Twomey and Berthold Kaempfert.

Moderately (in 2)

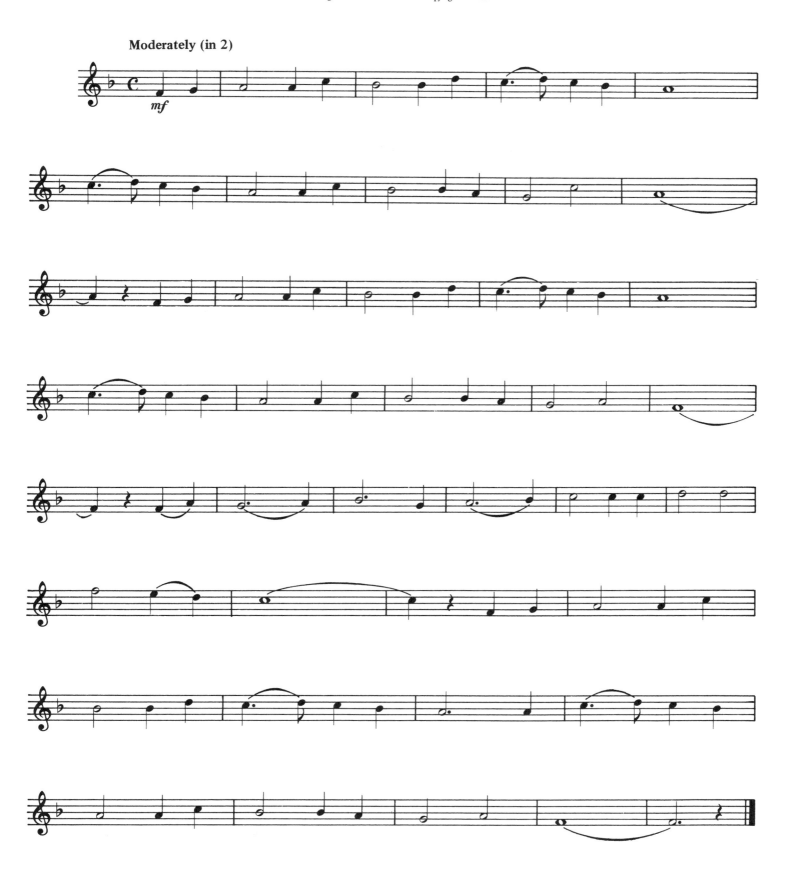

WE'LL MEET AGAIN

Words & Music: Ross Parker and Hughie Charles.

Moderato

WHISPERING GRASS

Words: Fred Fisher.
Music: Doris Fisher.

Moderato

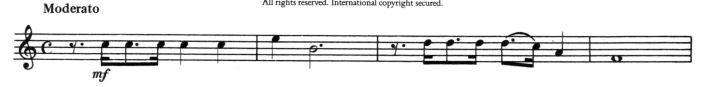

THE SONG FROM "MOULIN ROUGE"
also known as "Where Is Your Heart"

Words: William Engvick.
Music: Georges Auric.

YOU'RE THE DEVIL IN DISGUISE

Words & Music: Bill Giant, Bernie Baum and Florence Kaye.

WITHOUT A SONG

Words: William Rose and Edward Eliscu.
Music: Vincent Youmans.

THE WONDER OF YOU

Words & Music: Baker Knight.

Slowly, with feeling

YELLOW SUBMARINE

Words & Music: John Lennon and Paul McCartney.

YOU'RE GOING TO LOSE THAT GIRL

Words & Music: John Lennon and Paul McCartney.

Moderately

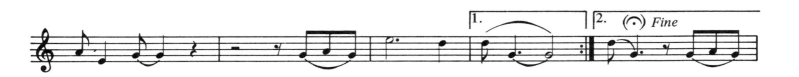

YESTERDAY

Words & Music: John Lennon and Paul McCartney.

7/90 (10401)